THE DEATH OF Archie®

Written by
Paul Kupperberg

Pencils by
**Pat Kennedy, Tim Kennedy
and Fernando Ruiz**

Inks by **Jim Amash, Bob Smith
and Gary Martin**
Lettering by **Jack Morelli**
Coloring by **Glenn Whitmore**

Cover Pencils by **Pat & Tim Kennedy**
Cover Inks by **Bob Smith**
Cover Coloring by **Tito Peña**

Based on the
Archie Wedding Series
originated by Michael Uslan

LIFE WITH ARCHIE: THE DEATH OF ARCHIE: A LIFE CELEBRATED COMMEMORATIVE ISSUE (ISSN: 2155-2304) Published by ARCHIE COMIC PUBLICATIONS, INC., 325 Fayette Avenue, Mamaroneck, New York 10543-2318. Jon Goldwater, Publisher/Co-CEO, Nancy Silberkleit, Co-CEO, Mike Pellerito, President, Victor Gorelick, Co-President. ARCHIE characters created by John L. Goldwater. The likenesses of the original Archie characters were created by Bob Montana. "Life With Archie" and the individual characters' names and likenesses are the exclusive trademarks of Archie Comic Publications, Inc. Copyright © 2014, Archie Comic Publications, Inc. All rights reserved. Nothing may be reprinted in whole or part without written permission from Archie Comic Publications, Inc. This periodical may not be sold except by authorized dealers and is sold subject to the conditions that it shall not be sold or distributed with any part of its cover or markings removed, nor in a mutilated condition, nor affixed to or as a part of any advertising, literary or pictorial matter whatsoever. No actual person is named or delineated in this fiction magazine and any similarities to real people and places in this fiction magazine are purely coincidental. Distributed in India by the Variety Book Depot, New Delhi – 110 001. E-mail: varietybookdepot@rediffmail.com. Periodicals postage paid at the post office at Mamaroneck, New York and at additional mailing offices. Title registered in U.S. Patent Office. POSTMASTER, send address changes to LIFE WITH ARCHIE, c/o Archie Comic Publications, Inc., 325 Fayette Avenue, Mamaroneck, NY 10543-2318. Printed in USA.

Publisher / Co-CEO: Jon Goldwater
Co-CEO: Nancy Silberkleit
President: Mike Pellerito
Co-President / Editor-In-Chief: Victor Gorelick
Chief Creative Officer: Roberto Aguirre-Sacasa
SVP – Sales & Business Development: Jim Sokolowski
SVP – Publishing & Operations: Harold Buchholz
SVP – Publicity & Marketing: Alex Segura
Executive Director of Editorial: Paul Kaminski
Production Manager: Stephen Oswald
Project Coordinator & Book Design: Joe Morciglio
Proofreader/Editorial Assistant: Jamie Lee Rotante
Additional Written Content: Alex Segura & Jamie Lee Rotante

THE BEGINNING OF AN END

Archie Andrews died as he lived—helping his friends, and showing the bravery and heart that we all hope is inside each of us.

The climactic ending of LIFE WITH ARCHIE, which you've just read, is an ending—but not the end for the character who's brought joy to millions around the world for almost 75 years. But it does signal the final chapter of one of the company's most critically-acclaimed series in LIFE WITH ARCHIE. Archie's heroic sacrifice in the face of a danger that many have faced in reality reiterates his role as a true everyman at any age. Archie is one of us—and one of the best, giving us all something to strive for. His final moments in the pages of LIFE WITH ARCHIE #36 is just the latest example of this.

While the issue is far from a happy affair, it does allow us—and in Riverdale, his own friends—the chance to celebrate the character and friend that we've come to know for all our lives. From the funny to the poignant, the issue not only presents Archie as a hero, but also shows us how the many important people that have filled his life see him: a friend, husband, teammate and colleague. Sometimes it's through absence that we truly realize how important something or someone is, as the second half of this story shows.

This ending also provides a rare opportunity in terms of characters with this kind of pop culture longevity—a chance to look back, to the beginning. Here, we meet Archie co-founder John L. Goldwater, who wanted to tell a story about an everyman teenager caught up in an ongoing, teenage love triangle. With those notes and more, he tasked young cartoonist Bob Montana with bringing his vision to life. Thus, Archie was born and comics—and entertainment—would never be the same.

OUR STORY SO FAR...

LIFE WITH ARCHIE tells the tale of two futures for everyman Archie Andrews: one where he's married to lovable girl-next-door Betty Cooper and another where he's married socialite Veronica Lodge. Both stories—under the sub-headers "Archie Marries Betty" and "Archie Marries Veronica"—were told separately in the pages of LIFE WITH ARCHIE magazine and conclude in the book you now hold in your hands.

But let's start from the top...

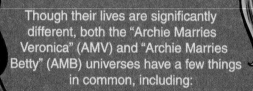

Though their lives are significantly different, both the "Archie Marries Veronica" (AMV) and "Archie Marries Betty" (AMB) universes have a few things in common, including:

Mr. Lodge is business partners with the evil tycoon Fred Mirth, who secretly has an agenda all his own. Dilton returns to Riverdale and conducts secret meetings with both men. It turns out that when they were in college, Mirth stole several of Dilton's scientific plans.

Also, in an effort to prevent the Chocklit Shoppe from closing, Jughead takes over with the help of his new girlfriend, Midge.

"AMV" starts with the newlyweds working for Lodge Industries. Meanwhile, Mr. Lodge and Fred Mirth are buying out all of Riverdale's local shops. Moose and Midge break up due to his anger issues. He finds peace through meditation then later becomes Mayor. Jughead—overwhelmed with running the newly-franchised Chocklit Shoppe disappears, putting more stress on Midge. She ends her relationship with Jughead. He starts dating Ethel and they later get married.

"AMB" begins with the couple moving back to Riverdale from NYC after Archie's music career stalls. Mr. Weatherbee marries Ms. Grundy, but she soon after succumbs to cancer. Archie and Betty then accept jobs as teachers at Riverdale High, with Archie teaching Music and Betty teaching English. Moose Mason also joins the ranks of Riverdale High Alumni now working at their alma mater as the new janitor. Midge and Jughead are married and have welcomed a baby boy to the world!

Archie's childhood pal Ambrose Pipps has been recruited by the "Good" Dilton of the AMB future to unite the two alternate timelines and save the day. He brings the two Archies, along with the AMB Reggie, to Memory Lane. The "Evil" Dilton from AMV was building something called a "Super Collider," that Fred Mirth got his hands on and was planning on using on the entire universe for sinister purposes. Fortunately, the Mr. Lodge of the AMB future built a failsafe device under Riverdale High in case the "Super Collider" had gone off. Moose, along with "Good" Dilton's help, destroys the super collider—erasing everyone's memories of the event! While this is taking place, Reggie and Archie are deemed missing in a "mine collapse," worrying everyone. When Archie returns safely in AMV, he and Veronica are reunited and put their rocky past behind them.

In AMV, Fred Mirth offers Archie a job as the head of a music label and Veronica quits Lodge Industries to start her own company, but she is framed by Mirth for corruption and is later arrested. Meanwhile, Betty and Reggie begin dating. Reggie opens his own antique motors shop, while Betty starts her own catering business. Reggie pitches a reality show to a TV producer about his life and relationship with Betty, which debuts at the cost of the couple's privacy.

In AMB, Archie begins to resent Betty's increasing responsibilities at school—where she's been promoted to Interim Assistant Principal, and he starts hanging out with Bella Beazly, Ms. Beazly's daughter and the new cafeteria cook at Riverdale High—who kisses him. Reggie and Veronica start dating, but the two manage to find a good balance between their relationship and their busy schedules.

In both universes, Kevin Keller returns to Riverdale after being injured during his tour of duty in the Middle East. Upon his return, he falls in love with, and later marries, his physical therapist, Clay Walker.

While attempting to stop a robbery, Clay is shot. He survives, and the event gets Kevin thinking about the nation's lax gun laws, and he decides to run for Senate!

A shooter later targets gay employees in an attack at the nearby Southport Mall, fueling Kevin's campaign for Senate on an anti-gun platform.

He wins the election, but his views have hurtled him into the spotlight—and not everyone agrees with his legislative plans.

In AMB, Jughead's sister, Jellybean, starts working at the Chocklit Shoppe and begins dating a mysterious stranger, who appears to be the cause of a string of robberies in Riverdale, until Jellybean turns him in after tries to rob the Chocklit Shoppe.

In both universes, the Chocklit Shoppe has endured the test of time and hosted the weddings of Mr. Weatherbee and Ms. Grundy, Svenson and Ms. Beazly, Jughead and Midge, Jughead and Ethel, the party for the debut of TV's "Betty Loves Reggie," and it will now serve as the after party location for Kevin's Southport fundraiser.

In AMB, Cheryl Blossom returns to Riverdale where she reveals her battle with a severe form of breast cancer. Veronica helps Cheryl out, holding a benefit concert at the newly-opened Chowhouse II. The fundraiser proves to be successful and she starts her own breast cancer awareness foundation.

All of these events bring us to the grand finale of LIFE WITH ARCHIE. Archie's final moments and the celebration of his life afterward are arguably the most poignant and engaging stories in a series full of wonderful, historic and dramatic moments. Read as a whole, it serves as the perfect coda to an epic tale of friendship, love, loss and humanity. Even read alone, it gives the reader a sense of what a trailblazing series LIFE WITH ARCHIE has been.

Turn the page and prepare for the final chapters of the life of Archie.

uh.

NO, SIR, I WON'T.

Hmph!

SO... I'LL SEE YOU AROUND, MR. P.! TAKE IT EASY.

JUST LIKE HIS FATHER.

I GUESS MAYBE THERE IS HOPE FOR THIS GENERATION AFTER ALL!

"THINK ABOUT YOUR FUTURE," MR. PAVIA SAID...

I'VE BEEN SO BUSY SWEATING MY *PRESENT* PROBLEMS THAT I HAVEN'T GIVEN MUCH THOUGHT TO WHAT'S AHEAD.

IT FEELS LIKE ONLY YESTERDAY WE WERE IN HIGH SCHOOL... BUT BACK THEN, *ONLY* THE *NOW* MATTERED.

I DOUBT IF I EVER EVEN CONSIDERED BEING WHERE I AM TODAY...

MEMORY LN.

8

OVER HERE, ARCH.! THE GREAT REGGIE MANTLE--*ALONE*? YOUR BETTER HALF FINALLY REALIZE THE FOLLY OF HER WAYS AND *DUMP* YOU?

NAW, I THINK *THIS* RELATIONSHIP'S A *KEEPER*!

IT SURE LOOKS THAT WAY TO THE REST OF US! SO... WHEN ARE YOU GONNA POP THE *BIG* QUESTION ?!

NOW YOU SOUND LIKE MY PARENTS.! BUT I THINK WE'RE GETTING THERE.

I JUST WANTED TO GET MY LIFE SORTED OUT BEFORE I MADE THE *BIG MOVE*!

GOOD THINKING. I'M NOT SORRY I GOT MARRIED WHEN I DID...

...BUT IT PROBABLY WOULD'VE BEEN A MUCH *SMOOTHER* RIDE IF I'D HAD A CLUE AND DID A LITTLE BIT MORE GROWING UP FIRST.

WAY I SEE IT, YOU'VE *BOTH* DONE A LOT OF GROWING UP LATELY. GOING THROUGH IT TOGETHER'S GOT TO HAVE MADE YOU STRONGER AS A COUPLE.

YEAH, I REALLY THINK IT HAS...

28

WOW! THE HOMETOWN CROWD REALLY DOES LOVE *KEVIN!*

HIS APPEAL'S BROADER THAN JUST RIVERDALE, BETTY. I THINK ONE OF THESE DAYS...

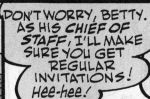

...WE MIGHT BE CALLING HIM *"MR. PRESIDENT!"*

HOW COOL WOULD *THAT* BE?! DO YOU THINK HE'LL INVITE US TO THE WHITE HOUSE?

DON'T WORRY, BETTY. AS HIS *CHIEF OF STAFF,* I'LL MAKE SURE YOU GET REGULAR INVITATIONS! *Hee-hee!*

ONLY CHIEF OF STAFF?! I DIDN'T THINK YOU'D SETTLE FOR ANYTHING LESS THAN *VICE PRESIDENT!*

WELL, I DIDN'T WANT TO SOUND *GREEDY!*

OH! THERE ARE THE BOYS!

I'VE GOT THE SENATOR COVERED... HOW'S IT LOOK, MOORE?

NOTHING TO REPORT SO FAR...

...BUT WITH THIS MANY PEOPLE PACKED IN HERE, IT'S HARD TO BE SURE!

...BUT WITH-OUT A DEFINITE THREAT ON THE TABLE, WE'RE ALL THE SENATOR GETS!

THEN WE'LL JUST HAVE TO BE *ENOUGH!*

I HEAR YOU, PARTNER--

--WE COULD'VE USED A FEW MORE EYES ON THINGS...

MAN, I GOTTA TELL YOU, EVEN THOUGH SHE'S MY WIFE, THAT LADY *STILL* TAKES MY BREATH AWAY!

YEAH, I KNOW WHAT YOU MEAN...

31

GET DOWN, CLAY!!

F.B.I.! OUT OF MY WAY!!

34

36

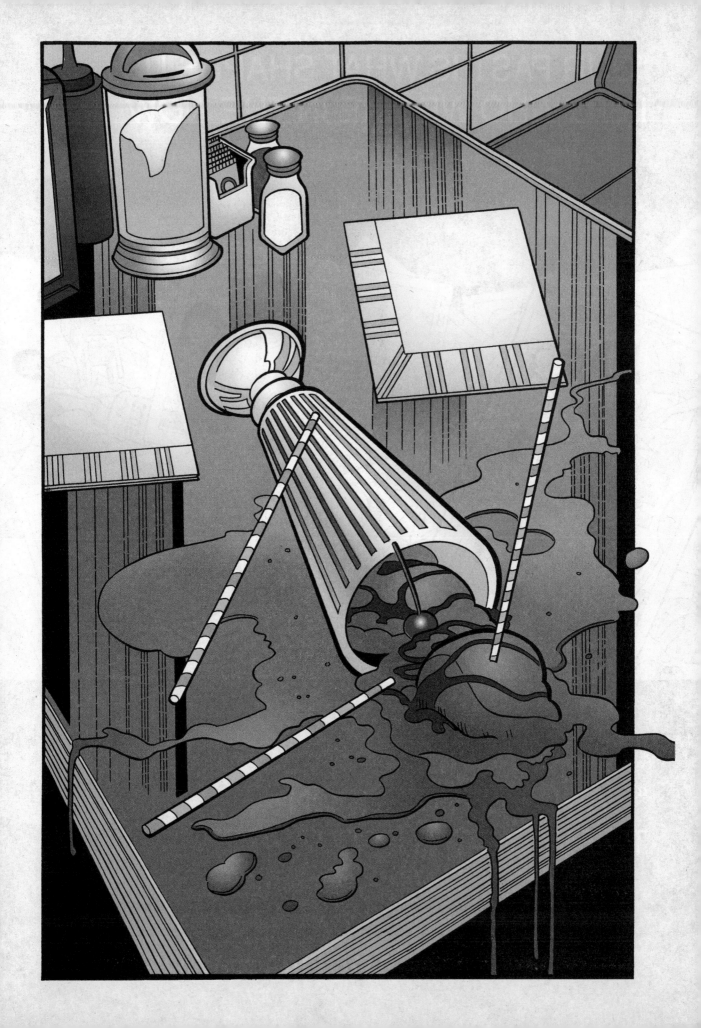

"OUR PAST IS WHAT SHAPES US INTO WHO WE ARE IN THE *NOW*..."

I TRIED TALKING TO HIM ABOUT IT, BUT HE TOLD ME IT WAS NONE OF MY BUSINESS AND HE'D TAKE CARE OF IT!

OH, I SEE. SO YOU DECIDED TO HELP HIM OUT YOUR-SELF...?

YEAH, WHEN I SAW HE HADN'T FIXED IT AFTER A WEEK, I CALLED MY COUSIN WHO HAS A PLUMBING COMPANY IN HARTSBURG.

HE AGREED TO DO THE WORK AND TELL MR. PAVIA THE TOWN HAD SENT THEM--

--AND I'M GONNA WORK FOR HIM UNTIL THE JOB'S PAID OFF!

I'M TOUCHED BY YOUR CONCERN FOR YOUR NEIGHBOR, ARCHIE. MR. PAVIA HAS GIVEN A LOT TO RIVERDALE, ALBEIT *GRUMPILY*...

...AND THE ENTIRE TOWN PITCHES IN TO DO WHAT WE CAN FOR HIM SINCE HE LOST HIS PENSION IN A COMPANY BANKRUPTCY!

BUT... AS OF TODAY, YOU ARE *RETIRED* FROM THE PLUMBING BUSINESS!

I'M GOING TO CALL THE MAYOR AND SEE ABOUT GETTING YOUR COUSIN PAID... AND *YOU'RE* GOING HOME TO MAKE UP THOSE FAILING GRADES!

YES, SIR... THANK YOU, SIR... I'LL GET RIGHT ON IT... FIRST THING AFTER A *NAP!*

8

BUT THE REAL CREDIT FOR SAVING THIS PARK HAS TO GO TO ARCHIE, WHICH I SUPPOSE IS FITTING... AS IT WAS AN *ANDREWS* IN THE 19ᵗʰ CENTURY WHO DONATED THE LAND TO THE TOWN FOR A PARK.

PICKENS PARK

THERE ARE THOSE WHO BELIEVE IT WAS AN ANDREWS WHO FIRST SETTLED IN RIVERDALE...

NOT *ME*, OF COURSE... I SAY IT WAS A *LODGE*, NO DOUBT! EITHER WAY, ARCHIE'S IS A DISTINGUISHED ANCESTRY--

"--AND HE SEEMED DESTINED TO START FOLLOWING IN HIS FAMILY FOOTSTEPS EARLY ON..."

THIS IS *PATHETIC!*

YEAH, SOMEBODY OUGHT TO *DO* SOMETHING ABOUT THIS!

MY DAD SAYS IT'S THE *TOWN'S* JOB, BUT BECAUSE OF THE ECONOMY, IT CAN'T AFFORD TO!

ISN'T THERE ANYTHING *WE* CAN DO?

LIKE WHAT? REPLANT STUFF? FIX BENCHES?

10

...EVER AGAIN HAVE THE CHANCE AT SUCH A *PRIME* PIECE OF REAL ESTATE AT THESE PRICES, GENTLE-MEN...

...SMACK DAB IN THE MIDDLE OF RIVERDALE AND READY TO DEVELOP AS WE PLEASE!

YOU JUST GET US *PICKENS PARK*, LODGE... WE'VE GOT OUR *PICK* OF WHAT TO REPLACE IT WITH!

THERE'S PROFIT IN THIS FOR *ALL* OF US, HIRAM!

OH, YES, INDEED, THERE IS...

MR. LODGE.

HELLO, ARCHIE. HAVE YOU GOTTEN LOST AGAIN?

12

IS...IS IT *TRUE*, MR. LODGE? WHAT YOU AND THOSE MEN WERE TALKING ABOUT?

ER...WHAT? WHAT DO YOU THINK YOU HEARD...?

THAT YOU WERE BUYING PICKENS PARK INTO A SHOPPING MALL OR SOMETHING?

YOU'RE ONLY *HALF* RIGHT, MY BOY. YES, I'M BUYING THE PARK BECAUSE THE TOWN NEEDS MONEY...

...BUT I HAVEN'T MADE *ANY* DECISIONS ABOUT WHAT'S TO BE DONE WITH IT.

WHY DOES ANYTHING HAVE TO BE DONE WITH IT? KIDS IN RIVERDALE NEED A PLACE TO *PLAY!*

IF THAT'S ALL THAT'S BOTHERING YOU, THEN YOU KIDS ARE *ALWAYS* WELCOME TO PLAY *HERE!*

YEAH, BUT MR. LODGE...

ENOUGH, ARCHIE! THIS IS GROWN-UP BUSINESS, DO YOU UNDERSTAND?

DID I HEAR RIGHT? DID DADDY SAY YOU GUYS WERE *WELCOME* HERE?

YEAH, BUT I DON'T THINK HE REALLY *MEANT* IT!

STILL... A PROMISE *IS* A PROMISE!

13

"... BACK IN THE DAYS WHEN I WAS THE PRACTICAL JOKER OF THE GROUP AND REGGIE PLAYED THE PART OF THE ARROGANT JOCK..."

I'LL KILL YOU, JONES!

YOU MADE A *FOOL* OF ME IN FRONT OF THE WHOLE CHEER-LEADING SQUAD...!

I KNOW, I KNOW! I COULD'VE WAITED AND YOU'D HAVE DONE IT *WITHOUT* MY HELP!

WHOA!

MAN, AREN'T YOU OVER-DOING THE HAIR PRODUCT, REGGIE?

IT'S NOT *FUNNY*, ARCHIE! I'VE *HAD* IT WITH YOUR NEEDLE-NOSED DORK PAL!

FROM NOW ON, YOU CAN EITHER HANG OUT WITH HIM... *OR* ME!

WHAT? LIKE I CAN'T BE FRIENDS WITH *BOTH* OF YOU?

HE SOUNDS LIKE HE *MEANS* IT!

AWWW, HE'LL GET OVER IT!

"--AND HAD IT RIGGED AGAINST ME WITH A BOTTLE OF *BHUT JOLOKIA*, THE *HOTTEST* CHILI PEPPER KNOWN TO MAN!"

Heh, Heh!

"HE SLOPPED ENOUGH OF THAT HOT SAUCE ON ONE OF MY BURGERS TO BURN THE AVERAGE HUMAN TONGUE TO CINDERS..."

"...AND ONE BITE WAS ALL TOOK!"

YEE-OUCH!

WATER'S NO GOOD FOR WHAT AILS YOU, JUG! YOU NEED AN ICE COLD GLASS OF *MILK* TO CUT THAT HEAT!

UNLESS THE MILK'S *ALSO* BEEN MIXED WITH *HOT SAUCE!*

Phhhfff-TH!!

20

CALM DOWN, MAN! HE WAS JUST...

NO! I'VE *HAD* IT WITH THAT LOUDMOUTH CREEP! BUT MAYBE HE'S *RIGHT!* MAYBE YOU *CAN'T* BE FRIENDS WITH US BOTH!

I... I CAN'T CHOOSE WHICH OF YOU *NOT* TO BE FRIENDS WITH!

WELL, YOU'RE GONNA *HAVE* TO! I'D HATE TO LOSE YOU AS A FRIEND, ARCH...

...BUT IT'S EITHER *HIM* OR *ME!!*

C'MON, REGGIE, A *REAL* FRIEND WOULDN'T ASK ME TO *CHOOSE!*

SO NOW I'M NOT A REAL FRIEND?

I DUNNO... BUT JUGHEAD'S SAYING THE SAME THING ABOUT *YOU*...

...MAYBE YOU'RE BOTH RIGHT... MAYBE I NEED TO THINK ABOUT WHO MY FRIENDS ARE...

"AND JUST LIKE THAT, WE ALL SEEMED TO LOSE TOUCH.

"REGGIE AND I BOTH SAID HELLO TO ARCHIE, AND HE REPLIED, BUT THAT WAS ABOUT ALL THE TALKING WE DID.

I'M STARVED, YOU GUYS! LET'S ORDER FIRST AND... HEY!

LOOK WHO'S HERE!

HEY, ARCHIE. YEAH, JUGHEAD AND I KIND OF REALIZED WE WERE BEING...WHAT'S THE WORD I'M LOOKING FOR?

JERKS, ARCHIE. WE WERE JERKS. ESPECIALLY REGGIE.

BUT, YOU KNOW HOW IT IS WITH PALS? YOU FIGHT... BUT THEN YOU MAKE UP!

SEE, THAT'S WHAT I ALWAYS THOUGHT...

...AND ME AND REGGIE HAVE BEEN BUDS EVER SINCE... EVEN IF WE DO GET ON EACH OTHER'S NERVES.

IRONIC, ISN'T IT, THAT ONE OF THE THINGS THAT WE BOND ON IS ALSO THE THING THAT MOST BUGS THE OTHER ONE?

THAT CAN'T BE THE MEANING OF FRIENDSHIP.

MAN, I HOPE NOT. I GUESS IT'S LIKE THE ARMY... THESE GUYS DRIVE YOU NUTS, BUT YOU COULDN'T LIVE WITHOUT THEM.

"SO ARCHIE DIDN'T ASK EITHER OF US!"

:SIGH!:

"HE *DID*, HOWEVER, ASK THE GIRL MOST IN *NEED OF A DATE--ETHEL MUGGS!*"

I ALWAYS THOUGHT YOU WERE BOTH HURT OR ANGRY THAT HE TOOK HER INSTEAD.

HOW? WE KNEW HE WAS JUST BEING A GOOD FRIEND... AND WE SAW HOW HAPPY IT MADE ETHEL.

EVEN THOUGH WE WERE ALWAYS SO COMPETITIVE, I THINK WE BOTH ALWAYS KNEW *HOW* IT WAS GOING TO TURN OUT.

YEAH, I THINK DEEP DOWN, WE KNEW THE TRUTH.

COME TO THINK OF IT, I GUESS EVERYBODY DID...!

YOU ARE CORRECT, MY DEAR, SO... LET US TARRY NO LONGER! ATTENTION, MY DEAR FRIENDS--

CLAP
CLAP
CLAP
CLAP

"--IT IS TIME THIS CELEBRATION *COMMENCED!*"

WELCOME TO RIVERDALE HK

MAN, NO MATTER HOW LONG I'M AWAY FROM THIS PLACE, EVERY TIME I COME BACK, IT'S LIKE COMING HOME!

YEAH, IT FEELS LIKE HALF MY LIFE TOOK PLACE HERE!

IT DID. HEY, REMEMBER-- THE ARCHIES PLAYED THEIR FIRST GIG HERE FOR THE FALL DANCE!

WHO CAN FORGET! WE WERE *AWFUL!*

REMEMBER WHEN ARCHIE GOT SUPER-GLUED TO A HOCKEY STICK TRYING TO SET A TRAP TO GET BACK AT REGGIE?

HEH! YEAH--HE DIDN'T SUSPECT THAT I'D GOTTEN TO THAT STICK *FIRST* WITH THE GLUE!

DUDE, THOSE WERE THE DAYS!

33

ARCHIE WAS THE PRODUCT OF *GENERATIONS* OF RIVERDALE UPBRINGING.

AN ANDREWS WAS ONE OF THE TOWN'S FIRST SETTLERS, AND ONE OF ARCHIE'S ANCESTORS LIVED IN RIVERDALE EVER SINCE.

IT'S NOT THE *PLACE* THAT MAKES THE MAN, THOUGH.

IT'S THE *PEOPLE* WHO BROUGHT HIM INTO THE WORLD AND GAVE HIM HIS MORAL VALUES.

IT'S THE MEN AND WOMEN WHO TAUGHT HIM AND *CONFIRMED* THOSE VALUES. IT'S THE FRIENDS AND FAMILY WHO HELD HIS HAND AND WHOSE HANDS *HE* HELD IN TIMES OF NEED.

THANK YOU, SENATOR KELLER!

AND TO ENSURE THAT ARCHIE REMAINS CARVED IN OUR MEMORIES ...

ARCHIE ANDREWS IS THE *PRODUCT* OF ALL OF US... JUST AS HE'S *PART OF US* ALL IN RETURN!

AND I CAN THINK OF NO MORE *HOPEFUL* NOTE FOR RIVERDALE'S FUTURE, MY FRIENDS, THAN THAT!

36

"AND THEREFORE NEVER SEND TO KNOW FOR WHOM THE BELL TOLLS..."

"IT TOLLS FOR THEE." BY JOHN DONNE. YEAH, WE JUST LEARNED THAT ONE IN ENGLISH CLASS!

WELL, IN CASE YOU WERE WONDERING IF YOU'LL REMEMBER IT AFTER THIS SEMESTER, THE ANSWER IS ...YEAH. PROBABLY.

BUT I HAVEN'T FORGOTTEN THOSE ICE CREAM SODAS I OWE YOU GUYS! IS CHOCOLATE OKAY?

MY FAVORITE!

I LOVE ANY FLAVOR!

OKAY, WE'LL START YOU OFF WITH CHOCOLATE, THEN SEE IF WE CAN TEST THE LITTLE LADY'S CLAIM.

TRY THAT ONE ON FOR SIZE!

Hmm...WHAT SHALL WE TRY NEXT...?

THE END

AFTERWORD

LIFE WITH ARCHIE started back in 2010, following the hit "Will You Marry Me?" storyline, which I worked on with Michael Uslan. At the time, I thought the idea of Archie getting married was crazy, but the more I thought about it, the more I realized it was a really good idea. Some people were upset when they thought that Archie was only proposing to one of the girls, which was why it was so important to create two realities where he marries them both. How did that happen? It all started when Archie took a walk up Memory Lane.

In my over fifty years of working at Archie, I've seen a lot of changes. We always try to keep up with the times and, especially in recent years, we've come up with some new things and a lot of big moves with the books, such as the creation of Kevin Keller. Introducing a gay teenager into the Riverdale family was huge. It was very big and very well received. It made sense that this character, who, in LIFE WITH ARCHIE, has become a bona fide hero, be the one who is saved by Archie. It has also been a great pleasure working with Jon Goldwater, who has not only shepherded in these important changes as well as this specific storyline, but also whose vision of the Archie universe is ever-expanding.

So, why did Archie have to die to save his friend? It's not because Riverdale has changed, or that the fundamental basics of what made Archie great have been altered—what's changed is reality. We have done some stories over the years that have dealt with bullying or other problems that kids might have in school, but never anything dealing with something like this. We've always said that Archie is a typical teenager—but in LIFE WITH ARCHIE he is a typical adult and, for better or for worse, has to face "adult" problems head on.

Yes, in LIFE WITH ARCHIE, Archie Andrews dies. It's a sad ending, but comic books are still here and Archie will live on in our comics, digests, graphic novels, digitally and in the not too distant future, TV and the movies. So wipe away your tears, Archie's still here and will be for years to come.

- Victor Gorelick,
Co-President / Editor-in-Chief

THE DEATH OF Archie®

A MESSAGE FROM THE PUBLISHER

I'd like to tell you a story...

It happened about five years ago. I'd just started at Archie as Co-CEO and found myself on the train back home. I'd brought some copies of the more recent comics with me to read on the commute. I ended up sitting next to a lady who seemed very intrigued by the books. Her eyes widened and she smiled. I felt like a million bucks—this lady knew Archie. She'd certainly be impressed when I told her I worked at the company.

"Wow, Archie—they still make those?"

My heart sank—but at the same time, my determination multiplied.

You see, I grew up with Archie and his friends. My father was on the ground floor of everything in relation to the character—Archie literally sprung from his mind onto the page! These characters were more than just artwork on a page to me. They were lifelong friends I now got to see every day. I never wanted to hear that lady's words again. I wanted everyone to know Archie—and what he stands for.

Archie, as a character and as a brand, has run parallel to the story of our country. From the final days of the Great Depression to the culture wars of the modern day, Archie has represented the best we have to offer: kindness, bravery, honesty and friendship. Sure, he stumbles and makes mistakes—don't we all? But despite a few pratfalls, his heart is in the right place.

The story today, five years later, is no longer "Wow, they still make those?" It's "What will Archie do next?" People know the brand. They know the character and his world and they expect the unexpected.

It started with the wedding and continued to LIFE WITH ARCHIE. The introduction of the first gay character in Archie comics, Kevin Keller, showed the world we meant business. His future marriage in the pages of LIFE WITH ARCHIE reiterated it. We were the first company to fully embrace digital comics and expand our reach to anyone with a tablet or computer. The company is no longer considered a novelty or retro. In fact, words like "vibrant," "progressive" and "innovative" are more likely to accompany mentions of the brand. We challenge our critics and aim for the stars. All in the quest to tell a great story and entertain our legion of fans.

At Archie Comics, there are no limits and there are no rules beyond the basic ones I laid out to my staff and supremely talented writers and artists when I started: Make Riverdale feel like a city in America today—reflective of our world. Keep our characters flexible and durable and stay true to what they've always been.

Today we have an older Archie at the center of an acclaimed, serialized drama series. We have a teenage Archie leading a band of friends against a zombie apocalypse. We have a younger Archie in animation and we will have iterations of Archie across media in the coming years. We will always have the classic teenage humor and slapstick that this company was built on—a legacy I carry with me that my father and his two co-founders began and a responsibility I've never taken lightly. Archie is everywhere.

Jon Goldwater
Publisher / Co-CEO

"As soon as we decided on having multiple variants for the Death of Archie, there was no question that we wanted to have art from the enormously talented Francesco Francavilla. From his work on one of the most notable variants we've published on this very title in LIFE WITH ARCHIE #23 to his art in AFTERLIFE WITH ARCHIE—both of these, in addition to this finale, were all ideas that came from the mind of the intrepid Jon Goldwater— it is clear how expertly he can depict a somber and striking scene, and this cover is no exception."

- Mike Pellerito
President, Archie Comics

"Great! My first-ever **ARCHIE** cover and Archie's nowhere to be seen. This may be the saddest drawing I've ever done. I felt like doing a nice, cheerful **PUNISHER** cover afterwards. It always takes me several covers to figure out how I should draw a character or characters."

"Having my first ARCHIE cover be such an important one, filled with gravitas, did not help! Somehow I got it done. Godspeed, Waffle-head. Godspeed."

- Adam Hughes

"The Death of Archie isn't something I ever expected to witness, but what a fitting way to end a serious and dramatic series! I've done some covers featuring the rock bands of Riverdale in the past, so I thought I'd continue the theme for this image—The Archies minus their frontman."

- Fiona Staples

"I feel a bit odd saying that I had a great time doing my first Archie drawing around the circumstances of his death. But it was a great time. He's such a giant icon and it was a huge thrill to do the cover."

- Michael Allred

The death of someone close is never a happy thing. Everyone we share our lives with we leave an impression on, a small thumbprint, for better or worse.

- Ramón K. Pérez

"Having Alex Ross do a cover for Archie was like a dream come true. His painted art is not only award-winning, but his images are so memorable it was a no-brainer that we wanted him to be a part of this historic finale."

"The final product is one that is sure to withstand the tests of time along with his many memorable covers."

- Mike Pellerito
President, Archie Comics

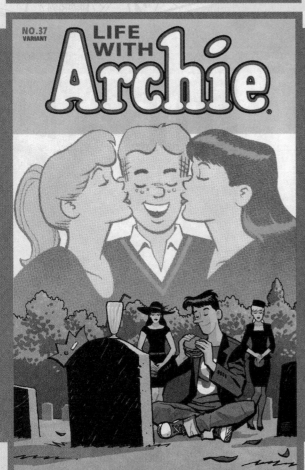

"As a fan, it was important to me to balance the solemnity of the occasion with some of the humor and life that Archie Comics are known for."

"While the resting crown hat on the tombstone is a signal to move on and grow up, I thought Jughead would also try to celebrate his best friend's memory the only way he knows how: with a burger and malt shake. It's a quiet, private moment between friends. Pour one out for Archie Andrews!"

- Cliff Chiang

"When I was approached by Archie Comics about drawing one of the covers for the Death of Archie, I gave the matter some serious thought. The books have always centered around the Archie/Betty/ Veronica relationship. I wanted a simple image, emblematic of that now sundered relationship between the three."

- Walter Simonson

"We love to incorporate Jill Thompson's art on our covers as much as we can. It was a pleasure having her be a part of this momentous occasion."

- Mike Pellerito,
President, Archie Comics

"I've always wanted to draw the Archie characters. It was quite an honor to try to tap into the emotional loss Betty and Veronica are wrestling with in this story."

- Tommy Lee Edwards

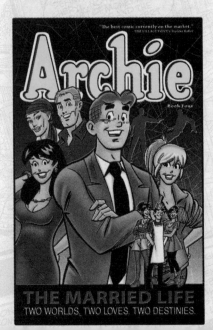